# LIFE SKILLS

# FEEL GOOD, LOOK GREAT!

Steve Parker

Heinemann
LIBRARY

**www.heinemannlibrary.co.uk**
Visit our website to find out more information about Heinemann Library books.

**To order:**
☎ Phone +44 (0) 1865 888066
🖨 Fax +44 (0) 1865 314091
💻 Visit www.heinemannlibrary.co.uk

Heinemann Library is an imprint of Capstone Global Library Limited, a company incorporated in England and Wales having its registered office at 7 Pilgrim Street, London, EC4V 6LB – Registered company number: 6695582

Heinemann is a registered trademark of Pearson Education Limited, under licence to Capstone Global Library Limited

Text © Capstone Global Library Limited 2009
First published in hardback in 2009
Paperback edition first published in 2011

Edited by Pollyanna Poulter
Designed by Philippa Jenkins and Hart MacLeod
Original illustrations © Pearson Education Limited by Medi-mation
Picture research by Elizabeth Alexander and Maria Joannou
Production by Alison Parsons
Originated by Modern Age Repro House Ltd.
Printed and bound in China by South China Printing Company Ltd.

ISBN 978 0 431112 45 9 (hardback)
13 12 11 10 09
10 9 8 7 6 5 4 3 2 1

ISBN 978 0 431112 61 9 (paperback)
15 14 13 12 11
10 9 8 7 6 5 4 3 2 1

**British Library Cataloguing-in-Publication Data**
Parker, Steve, 1952-
Feel good, look great. - (Life skills)
613.7'043
A full catalogue record for this book is available from the British Library.

**Acknowledgements**
We would like to thank the following for permission to reproduce photographs: © Alamy: pp. **5** (Digital Vision/Nancy Ney), **7** (Ambient Images Inc), **9** (Peter Casolino), **30** (Somos Images LLC), **33** (Corbis Super RF/Timothy Tadder), **35** (Image Source Pink), **39** (Marwood Jenkins), **40** (PHOVOIR /FCM Graphic), **47** (Daniel Dempster Photography); © Corbis: pp. **13** (Julia Grossi/Zefa), **15** (Volker Moehrke/Zefa), **16** (Envision), **43** (Peter Turnley); © Getty Images: pp. **11** (Iconica), **24** (Stone/Erik Snyder), **27** (Stone), **37** (Stone/Bruce Ayres), **49** (Image Bank/Brooklyn Productions); © iStockphoto: p. **22**; © PA Photos: pp. **19** (Martin Rickett), **21** (CSM/Landov); © Rex Features: pp. **28** (J.Norlander/IBL), **45** (Sipa Press).

Cover photograph of smiling man with a slice of melon reproduced with permission of © Corbis (MedioImages).

Every effort has been made to contact copyright holders of material reproduced in this book. Any omissions will be rectified in subsequent printings if notice is given to the Publishers.

# Contents

Some words are printed in bold, **like this**. You can find out what they mean by looking in the glossary.

# FACE THE WORLD

Like everyone, now and again you have a rough day. Everything seemingly goes wrong – you lose something important, perform poorly in an exam, forget to text a friend, miss a favourite programme, and then end up with a pounding headache. Life can be unfair, and sometimes it feels like the world is against you.

## WHAT YOU THINK

But is life really so unfair? Is it really everyone else, and everything else, that's against you? Or is it you? Could you have done better? Maybe you tried to do too much in a rush. Perhaps you got distracted by other matters and wasted time, rather than focusing on what you should have been doing.

Think about how other people might see you during "one of those days". Chances are you looked irritated and annoyed. This will not have gone unnoticed by your family and friends. It may have made them feel concerned about you not being your usual self. Or perhaps they may have simply reflected your irritation and annoyance right back at you.

### What you feel

The way that you feel on the inside has a huge effect on how you look on the outside. The way you behave, the decisions you make, your physical appearance, even the way you walk, all affect how other people see you, treat you, and react to you. This happens much more than most people realise.

Feeling good on the inside often helps to put the world back on your side. You may think that feeling good isn't all that easy, but making this happen is actually quite straightforward.

- Exercise, keep fit, and eat properly.
- Try to understand your thoughts and feelings – and think before you act.
- Avoid taking unnecessary risks.
- Learn more about the pressures of modern life (from family, friends, teachers, adverts, and the media) and how to best deal with them.

As you begin to feel better on the inside, you'll look better on the outside. Other people will take notice. It will affect the way you enjoy each day, make friends, cope with setbacks, view the world, and gain confidence.

## Getting it **Right**

Many people bottle up their thoughts and opinions, especially when they feel that something bothering them is abnormal. The fact is that feelings like these are quite normal. Having personal questions that you are afraid to ask is normal, too. And, as this book shows, the answers to all these worries are almost always reassuringly, well, normal.

*Feeling good about yourself rubs off on others and happiness spreads quickly between friends. Being miserable can bring everyone down and no one wants the blame for that.*

*"One kind of happiness is to know exactly at what point to be miserable."*

Francois de la Rochefoucauld (1613–1680), French writer

# Eat Well, Feel Good

It may be a cliché, but on many levels it is true: you are what you eat. Eating properly is one of the easiest, fastest, and best ways to good health. The foods you consume and the eating habits you develop don't just affect the way you will feel this evening, tomorrow, or next week. Food and eating have huge results for your health long into the future.

## Eating excuses

Have you ever heard someone blurt out an excuse as to what they are eating and why? Consider some of the ways that people think about food.

- I had to eat fast, I only had two minutes.
- I always just eat the same things as my friends.
- I was so busy talking, I can't remember what I ate.
- I ordered the hottest, spiciest dish to impress my friends.
- I couldn't be bothered to think about what I wanted, or do any cooking, so I grabbed some crisps.

Do you ever think about food like this? Do you think your body appreciates what you feed it?

**Write down some of the things you've said about food. Then take a good, hard look to examine why you eat the foods you eat and why you eat them the way you do.**

TIP

### Food for thought

Willpower and determination are involved in eating properly and it always helps to think of the benefits. No one feels right when they eat the wrong food.

How and what you eat impacts on how you feel and look. The condition of your skin, the size of your muscles and bones, your weight, and your ability to concentrate are all affected by food.

Eating can be a great social event. People often use meal times as a way to meet and catch up on each other's news. If you want to get to know someone, try arranging a meal together. You can always discuss your likes and dislikes if you get stuck for something to say.

## Getting it Wrong

Some people eat when they are bored. They eat because it gives them something to do and something to think about, not because they are hungry. Before long, boredom eating can become a nasty habit. As with any habit, recognising you have one puts you halfway to overcoming it. Boredom eaters often simply need to find another way to fill their time, perhaps by taking a brisk walk or ringing a friend for a chat.

## Habit and routine

Healthy eating is largely a matter of habit and routine. Some people simply drift into unhealthy eating habits without realising it. With some knowledge and understanding, they can get back to ways of healthy eating and retrain themselves into a more suitable, balanced approach.

# WHY EAT?

Food is not something that we eat simply for its flavours. Food is vital for the body's inner workings. Knowing what is in food and how it keeps the body healthy is important when working towards a balanced diet. It also helps you to decide whether or not it is okay for you to eat something.

All foods are comprised of nutrients and substances from six main food groups.

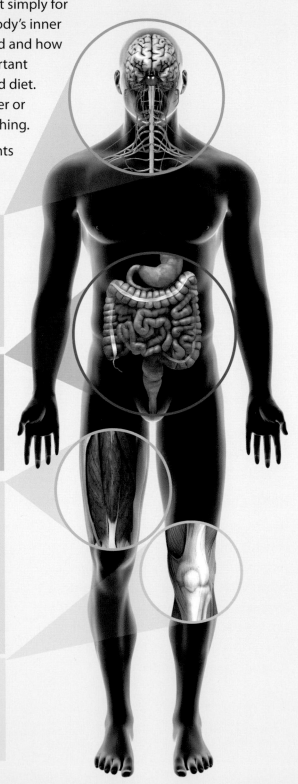

### 1. Fats and oils
Small amounts of **fats** are used both for building nerves and microscopic cells, and for energy if carbohydrates are lacking. Fats and oils are found in red meat, oily fish, eggs, dairy products, and certain plant foods, such as avocados, olives, peanuts, and soya.

### 2. Fibre
**Fibre** is roughage that helps the intestines work properly, satisfies hunger, and reduces risks of constipation and diseases, including certain cancers. Fibre is found mainly in plant foods, especially fresh fruits and vegetables.

### 3. Carbohydrates
**Carbohydrates** are energy foods used for life processes, especially muscle movements. Carbohydrates are found in rice, wheat, barley, and other cereals or grains. As well as products made from these, such as pasta and bread. Starchy vegetables, such as potatoes, also contain carbohydrates, as do bananas, strawberries, and sugary items, such as sweets and chocolate.

### 4. Minerals
**Minerals** are necessary for strong bones and teeth, and to ward off disease. They are found in a wide range of foods, especially fresh fruits and vegetables.

### 5. Proteins

**Proteins** are "building foods" which make up the main structure of muscles, bones, skin, and most other body parts. They are found in meat, poultry, fish, eggs, dairy products, nuts, soybeans, and other beans and peas.

### 6. Vitamins

Body processes work and stay healthy with the help of **vitamins**, which are also used to maintain clear skin and ward off disease. They are found in a wide range of foods, especially fresh fruits and vegetables.

## Getting it Right

Try tweaking a meal to make it healthier. Take fried chicken and chips, for example. If you have grilled or roasted chicken it is just as tasty, but has a fraction of the fat of fried chicken. Chuck out the chips in favour of mashed or roasted potatoes, or substitute a vegetable in place of a handful of chips.

*It is hard to complain about food being boring and tasteless when there's so much choice and variety.*

## Food labelling

Food labels can be complicated. Labels often include long lists of percentages of ingredients, and some show how many micrograms of each are needed daily. Most people are too busy to study and understand food labelling. In general, the main eating guidelines on labels are more important than looking up exact details, unless a food **allergy** is involved.

- Look at how labels advise on serving sizes.

- In general, choose foods low in sugar, fat, and salt.

- **Calories**, or joules, are measures of energy in foods. The more there are, the more energy you take in. If you don't use up the calories you take in, they eventually get turned into fat.

# WHAT THE EXPERTS SAY

Opinions and advice about diet and healthy eating often differs among the experts. As well as the basic guidelines, many experts study certain types of food, such as fruits, dairy produce, or carbohydrates. They each develop their own opinions with detailed suggestions about what is best for us. It can seem very confusing and often overwhelming. So, to start, it's best to focus on the basics.

## TIP

To enjoy your food:

- Take the time to chew, taste, and savour what you eat.

- Try something new. Modern food shops and supermarkets have a vast range of foods, including fresh fruits, vegetables, salads, and nuts. Why not try a new food item each week?

- Look out for seasonal bargains. Food in season tastes better and is usually less expensive than at other times of the year.

## Healthy guidelines

Here are some of the main healthy-eating guidelines. These guidelines are general, so there is no need to be a complete perfectionist about them, but it is important to bear them in mind. Following the guidelines keeps you healthy and feeling good inside.

## Eat five a day

"Five-a-day" refers to five helpings, portions, or servings of fresh fruits or vegetables each day. These should provide the body with all the vitamins and minerals it needs for healthy skin, bones, teeth, and other parts, as well as energy.

## Avoid ready-mades

Pre-prepared and ready-made meals can be a quick and easy alternative. However, they often contain high levels of sugar, salt, and other unwanted ingredients. A homemade meal, prepared with fresh ingredients, is not only healthier but is also often tastier and more affordable.

## Limit processed foods

Processed meats can often be found in hamburgers, sausages, ground-meat, doner kebabs, and salamis. Some processed meats are laden with fat, which isn't good for maintaining weight control or a healthy heart. Such meats also often contain high salt levels, which can affect **blood pressure**.

*Keeping your body hydrated is very important. Sip water throughout the day and – if you are exercising – increase the amount to avoid dehydration.*

## Eat three meals daily

You've probably heard it before, and that's because it is true: breakfast is an important meal. It refuels the body after a long night. The body is designed for several meals throughout the day, not just one massive, heaped plate of food and not much else in between. Going for too long between meals can make you light-headed, slow to react, and less able to focus and concentrate.

## DID YOU KNOW?

A typical human body needs about 2.5 litres (half a gallon) of water daily. Some of this is in our food, but most is in drinks. Take a drink of water whenever you feel thirsty, rather than letting your thirst build. Sipping water often is better than gulping it all at once during the day. Water is by far the best and cheapest drink. Colas, specialist sports drinks, and similar products are more expensive and usually contain sugar and **additives**.

## DID YOU KNOW?

There are many food myths and legends that are not true.

*Chocolate and fried food gives you spots.* There is no proven link between the two. The sugar in chocolate products can cause weight gain and rot teeth, while fried foods are linked to weight gain and heart problems.

*Potatoes are fattening.* How fattening a potato is depends on how you cook it (boiled or baked is healthier than fried) and how many you eat.

*Eating late at night is more fattening.* Time doesn't alter the calories in food. But if you eat and go to bed you won't burn off the calories. Also, if you are eating late it might mean you snack through the day to keep your energy levels up. This will up your total food intake.

*You can tell how fattening food is by its weight.* This is completely untrue. A typical slice of bread has about 70 calories, a medium potato about 80, but a tablespoon of mayonnaise has 100!

## MAKING SENSE OF IT ALL

Is there too much dietary advice? Are we bombarded by so many healthy eating guidelines that it's impossible to remember them, let alone follow them? Do some of the guidelines contradict each other? The answer to all these questions is "yes".

### Fads and fashions

Depending on what's in the news this week, food fads and fashions come and go. In 2006, world cancer experts announced that eating lots of processed meats increases the risk of certain forms of cancer. The experts advised avoiding these meats, and limiting all meat intake. This news reinforced earlier advice to limit processed meats as they can be high in fat and salt – and you can never be sure what meat is in there anyway!

### Vitamin and mineral pills

Do you need **dietary supplements** such as vitamin pills, mineral tablets, and nutrient powders? The short answer is "no". If you eat a balanced diet, with plenty of fresh fruit and vegetables, then you do not need supplements. (Unless you have a particular medical condition and your doctor has advised you take them.)

*Make time for meals. You can refuel your body and spend quality time with family and friends.*

**Getting it Right**

To ensure healthy eating:

- Eat a wide variety of foods for different tastes and flavours, and to maintain your interest in foods and how they affect your body.

- Eat five or more vegetables and fruits each day, along with wholegrain products.

- Limit foods rich in fats, especially **saturated fats**, found mainly in red meat, rich dairy products, and fried and processed foods.

- Limit your sugar intake. Sugars are found in many sweet foods, from sticky buns to chocolate bars.

- Avoid eating too much salt. Do not add salt to your food at the table and avoid ready-salted products, such as crisps, nuts, and popcorn.

- Have regular mealtimes and don't skip breakfast.

- Get plenty of physical activity.

# EATING PROBLEMS

Ask doctors about the major health problem in the developed world today, and most would answer with one word: obesity. The solution to this health problem is a simple one: eat healthily and exercise more. But many people look for more complicated reasons why they are overweight or obese, such as convincing themselves they have a body chemistry disorder. Though such conditions do exist they are exceptionally rare.

Common eating disorders in the developed world also include anorexia and bulimia. These can affect anyone, including boys and men. Look out for the following warning signs – if any of them apply to you and your eating habits you could be developing an eating disorder. Do you:

- often make excuses for why not to eat, such as being too busy with homework, have already eaten, or are feeling ill?

- eat odd combinations of food, often with strange excuses, such as "magical" health benefits?

- take lots of diet pills, indigestion treatments, laxatives, or similar?

- find you often lose weight and wear baggy clothes to disguise your size?

- become obsessed with your body image and often mention certain parts of your body, such as your thighs or stomach?

- take up weird exercise routines, risky sports and dares, and consume drugs and alcohol?

Eating disorders don't often go away by themselves and need prompt help from a medical professional.

**For a healthy weight:** **TIP**

- **Follow healthy eating guidelines and avoid fatty foods such as chips, crisps, and processed meats;**

- **Say no to snacks;**

- **Recognise and shed habits, such as comfort or boredom eating;**

- **Avoid situations where you might be tempted to eat extra food;**

- **Take regular exercise to burn up the energy in unwanted body fat;**

- **Tailor all this to your routine, so it's easy and fits in naturally.**

*Crash diets and phases of not eating have few plus sides – other than reducing the amount of washing-up.*

## Dieting

The best type of diet follows the recommended guidelines, as outlined in this chapter, and includes some form of regular exercise.

Crash diets, fashion diets, and diet pills are not nearly as successful. They tend to take up time (preparing strictly outlined "meals"), cost money (such as for special ingredients) and disrupt routines (for example, fasting and feasting).

Celebrities can sometimes be seen as promoting such a diet. However, it is questionable as to if they are being paid to do so and whether or not they even actually follow the diet themselves! A sensible, long-term approach to losing weight is always the better option.

### Getting it Right

If you struggle with snacking, set some ground rules and challenge yourself to stick to them. For example, allow yourself limited snacks when you successfully achieve meeting the recommended daily intake of fruits and vegetables, or after you undertake a regular exercise programme. When someone offers you a snack, have a reply ready, such as "No thanks, I've just eaten" or "I'm eating properly soon". Reply straight away. If you begin to consider the offer, you might be tempted! Remember that occasional snacking is fine, just don't let it get out of hand.

## At ease with food

Part of looking good is feeling at ease with who you are on the inside. When it comes to food, it helps to know about different kinds of foods and meals, and what you are putting into your body. One of the best ways to do this is to prepare your food yourself.

Whether cooking for yourself or others, cooking is great "me time". There are endless recipe books for simple snacks and easy meals that use fresh, healthy ingredients. You never know, you might enjoy cooking and become a celebrity chef!

## Food allergies

Some people react to foods that have no harmful effect on most people. The main culprits are milk, eggs, peanuts, "tree" nuts (such as walnuts), fish and shellfish, soya, and wheat.

### Getting it Right

To identify a food allergy, keep a food diary. Write down what you eat to see if your symptoms occur after a certain food. Eat natural, fresh, whole foods while you do this. Avoid ready meals and processed foods as you can never be sure of their ingredients. If the symptoms follow a pattern, cut out that food. As always, it's best to check with a doctor if you have any concerns.

*Some of the more common foods that can cause reactions in people.*

## DID YOU KNOW?

Symptoms of food allergies include: skin reactions, such as swelling, itching, and **flushing**; vomiting and/or diarrhoea; wheezing or coughing; runny nose, swollen lips, and sore, red, itchy eyes. Indigestion, or tummy pains, is not a common reaction to a food allergy.

# QUIZ

## ARE YOU A HEALTHY EATER?

1) **Which of the following best describes how you start your day?**
   a) I don't usually eat breakfast because I prefer to lie-in.
   b) I run out the door while inhaling a cream cake.
   c) I can't survive the morning without sitting down to breakfast first.

2) **When would you feel good about snacking?**
   a) Never. Snacking is far too fattening.
   b) Anytime!
   c) On occasion, when I want a special treat.

3) **How do you normally feel after lunch?**
   a) Sleepy and drained.
   b) Like I've had a serious sugar rush!
   c) Ready for the rest of the day.

4) **By mid-afternoon, how do you normally feel?**
   a) Bored and uninspired.
   b) Anxious and agitated.
   c) Full of energy.

5) **When do you normally eat dinner?**
   a) There is no normal for me.
   b) When I can fit in a bag of crisps — usually a big feast before bed.
   c) I sit down to a healthy meal every evening.

See page 50 to find out if your eating habits make you a healthy eater!

# Get Fit, Keep Fit

Physical fitness is not only a great way to stay healthy, look good, and avoid health problems. It is also a tremendous way to build confidence and develop a positive approach to life. As your fitness improves, worrying about your physical state is replaced by feeling more self-assured and proud of your body.

## REACHING YOUR GOALS

The goal here is not to become a world-class athlete (unless that is what you want to strive for). Instead, choose an activity – or variety of activities – that you enjoy doing, and set realistic goals. Each person is unique, with a different body and different physical abilities. Exercising with friends can be fun and is a helpful way to encourage one another. But remember to set goals for yourself, rather than comparing yourself with others.

## Benefits of fitness

Being physically fit helps with so many aspects of health, from weight control to strengthening your body. It benefits the heart, lungs, muscles, joints, and many other body parts – not just for now but way into the future. Exercise also helps you to feel good on the inside. It releases natural body substances called **endorphins** that affect the brain. These can give people a "buzz" and should make you feel elated and in a great mood after physical activity.

### Getting it Wrong

Avoid falling into the trap of comparing yourself to an unattainable ideal! It is vital to remember that nature has not given everyone the body shape, proportions, and physique of "Mr Universe" or "Miss World". Nor has nature given us each an airbrush, as used by the media to make models look perfect on paper. The key is to create inner confidence and to feel good about yourself. Other people will notice and appreciate that.

**For keeping and staying fit:**

- Exercise for at least 20 minutes each session.

- Exercise at least three sessions each week.

- Spend a few minutes stretching before and after exercise, to warm up and cool down your body.

- Get breathless, so your lungs work harder and faster.

- Raise your heartbeat, which you can check by taking your wrist pulse.

- Allow a few minutes to cool down and get your breath back after intense exercise.

- Wear suitable clothing or **kit**, and have a bottle of water handy – for sipping, not gulping.

*Exercise is great for feeling good on the inside, which makes you look happy on the outside. It is also an excellent way to share the fun, pleasure, and achievement with others, as well as keeping fit.*

## WHAT'S BEST FOR YOU

What type of exercise or activity suits you? Everyone is different. We each have our own situation, lifestyle, and natural abilities. Finding the right type of training or sport for you as an individual may take a bit of thought. You'll probably need to try out various activities to settle on one or two you like best. Or just keep it simple, and take a walk!

Before finalising which sport is for you, pause to think about the kit, equipment, **facilities**, and training. This is a crucial area, especially in high-speed, high-impact sports such as football, rugby, skiing, and snowboarding. Taking chances with your body and future health, perhaps even risking crippling injury, should not be an option. Get into an organised club or group that has the proper coaching, equipment, and know-how.

## Try-outs

Don't be put off if you have a go at one form of exercise and don't like it. There are hundreds to choose from. Some people like the thrill of fast, physical action, such as American football, ice-hockey, or snowboarding. Others prefer lower-impact sports such as swimming, dance, and yoga.

Can you put up with wind, rain, mud, and cold? If so, field sports, such as football and rugby, may be worth considering. But if you prefer being warm and dry then perhaps basketball, badminton, or working out in a gym is best. Whatever you choose, trying different activities and having a go is all part of the fun. Whatever you do, you should enjoy it. Otherwise you'll gradually lose enthusiasm, start to skip sessions, let down your teammates and end up on the couch.

## Popular choices

These are some of the more popular sporting choices made worldwide.

- With more than 3.5 billion people regularly playing or watching, football is the most popular.

- With over 2 billion people involved, cricket follows closely and is the main sport of India, Pakistan, Australia, and the Caribbean.

- Field hockey has 2 billion regular players and watchers, tennis has 1 billion, and volleyball and table-tennis have 900 million each.

American football is fast and tough. Without proper kit and training, the injury rate would be sky-high.

## DID YOU KNOW?

The most popular UK sport is football. It also claims the most reported sports injuries – about $\frac{1}{3}$. Rugby accounts for $\frac{1}{7}$ of reported injuries. However, in some areas, 50 times more teenagers play football than rugby. About $\frac{1}{4}$ of youngsters aiming to play professional sports have to quit because of injury. So look after yourself!

Source: Barclays Spaces for Sports project

"Most American football players are temperamental. That's 90 percent temper and 10 percent mental!"

Doug Plank, former Chicago Bears player and American football coach.

# HEALTH BENEFITS

As you become fitter and healthier, your muscles, senses, and coordination improve. Your reflexes and reactions become sharper, which means you have a lower risk of experiencing accidents and injuries. In terms of weight control, any activity burns off the energy in food, whereas a lack of activity turns it into fat.

When you exercise, your heart beats faster and stronger, keeping its special **cardiac** muscle in good condition. Also, your lungs are able to breathe fast and deeply, keeping airways clear and breathing muscles in good condition.

When you exercise, increased blood flow keeps major **blood vessels** clear and elastic, preventing blockage or hardening of their walls.

When you exercise, your muscles become less likely to get strained or pulled, and their increasing strength and stamina demand more oxygen from the lungs and blood from the heart, keeping these parts of your body fitter.

When you exercise, your joints become more supple and stronger, with less pain and stiffness, making them better able to shrug off **sprains**.

## Making time

Arrange activity and exercise into your daily routine so that it fits in easily, without too much fuss and special treatment. While it is always good to take on a challenge, the point is to make it fun first. Remember to take advantage of what you have in the way of abilities and facilities, rather than yearning after something that is too difficult.

## Body mass index

Body Mass Index, or BMI, is a link between a person's height and weight. It takes into account a person's height, so gives better indication of a person's size than weight alone. BMI does not strictly apply to babies and children, however, and forms only a small part of understanding your overall health.

Getting it **Right**

Exercise and sport don't need to be formal and highly arranged. You can grab them at almost any time, as the chance arises. Little bits of extra activity through the day add up to a valuable workout.

- Take the stairs rather than the lift or escalator.
- Cycle to places rather than sit in a car or bus.
- Get off the bus a stop early and take a refreshing walk.
- Grab exercise opportunities, such as a casual kick-about with friends in the park, or a fast walk to the shops or movies.
- Get others to join you – make it social and fun.

## DID YOU KNOW?

You can work out your BMI. Your BMI = your weight in kilograms divided by your height in metres, divided by your height in metres again

If you have a BMI of:

- less than 18.5, you are underweight for your height.
- between 18.5 and 25, you are a healthy weight for your height.
- between 25 and 30, you are overweight for your height.
- over 30, you are considered clinically obese.

If you're worried about being overweight or underweight, talk to your parents, school health worker, or doctor.

# ALL IN THE ACTION

The many benefits of exercise include not only keeping fit, gaining confidence, feeling better inside, and having more energy. Exercise helps your mind, too. As your performance improves, you'll realise that you have plenty of potential. You should also develop the knack of feeling more positive and wanting to achieve more, rather than feeling negative and giving up.

Team games don't only encourage friendships, they also help you to recognise certain traits in people, such as if they are reliable, helpful, and trustworthy.

## Getting it Wrong

True champions are very rare, so when exercising or competing, it's not helpful to measure your latest performance against the world's best. Doing so will only drag you down. Instead, measure your performance against your own previous efforts. It is important not to aim too high, too fast. Set out a series of sensible goals that you can achieve. Then you'll recognise that you're steadily improving, and gain pride from your success.

## Exercise and stress

Exercise is time out from daily worries and pressures. It frees your mind from those pressures and occupies it with other matters, such as gaining a new skill or concentrating on achieving a goal. This break from everyday stress is helpful. Often, afterwards you can face a problem with renewed energy and find a way to solve it.

## Exercise and your social life

Many sports and exercises involve other people, whether they are coaches, teammates, or opponents. The social aspects of sport mean that you are likely to meet new people, share interests, and make new friends.

As a member of a team you work together with others to achieve goals and, in doing so, feel that you belong.

## Exercise and the big sleep

Exercise and keeping fit help people to sleep more easily, and gain the right type of sleep through the night. A body that has seen plenty of action through the day is ready for a rest at night. Still, if you have trouble falling asleep – perhaps because you are worrying or dwelling on problems – then try to change your thoughts. Reflect on how satisfying your day has been and the good things you have achieved.

## Exercise and what others see

Exercise and activity have positive effects that other people will notice about you.

- As your muscles strengthen, your posture improves. So you'll be able to stand without stooping and walk without shuffling.

- Your coordination will improve and your reactions will be sharper, so you'll feel less clumsy and move in a smoother, more positive way.

- Exercise refreshes you, so you will look more aware and attentive than without it.

## WHAT TYPE OF SPORT?

1) **Which of the following sentences best describes your relationships with others?**
   a) I feel bored and lost when I'm all by myself.
   b) I like to hang out with friends, but also enjoy time on my own.
   c) I most prefer being on my own.

2) **A neighbour offers to give you a lift to school because it's raining and cold. Just as you're getting into the car, a friend calls by to walk to school with you. Do you:**
   a) decide to walk with your friend?
   b) ask your neighbour if she would mind taking your friend, too?
   c) take the lift and meet your friend at school?

3) **In science class, you are asked to follow directions to complete an experiment. You are given the option to work on your own or with a partner. Do you:**
   a) choose a partner you know you can rely on?
   b) work with a partner step-by-step through the directions?
   c) work independently?

**See page 50 to find out what type of sport you might like!**

# How You Feel Inside

Some people avoid exposing their innermost feelings and private emotions, even to those to whom they are closest. They tend to bottle up worries and cover up thoughts, thinking that perhaps this makes them tougher or impresses their friends. Sometimes, however, it is important to express feelings or emotions, especially when something is bothering you.

## HOLDING IT IN

Imagine someone starts to become withdrawn and remote. They don't join in or chat about what is going on, and they seem unable to loosen up and have a good time. A person like this probably wouldn't be much fun. You might start to avoid them and be reluctant to invite them to join you.

Now imagine that this person is you. You might think that you'd soon recognise these changes in yourself. But part of suppressing worries and feelings is not being aware of what is happening to you and around you. Your mind and mental state affects your behaviour, which other people see and react to. If you can't feel good on the inside, it's harder to look good on the outside.

## • CHECKLIST •

Some signs that show you may be **preoccupied** and withdrawn:

- Someone asks you something, but you do not hear what they've said.

- You catch yourself staring at nothing in particular, maybe gazing at the ground or into the distance.

- Good friends are often asking if you feel all right or if there's anything wrong.

- You lose interest in things you're usually keen on, such as sports or computer games.

## Getting it Right

Depending on your situation, try to find someone you can talk to. It helps if this is someone you feel close to, you think you can trust, and who has experience, such as:

- a parent or guardian,
- a trusted teacher, school **counsellor**, or mentor,
- a trusted, close relative, such as an aunt or uncle,
- a coach or trainer,
- a very good friend,
- an organisation that helps people cope.

## Thinking time

The trick is to take the time to look closely at yourself. Think about whether or not you have any inner worries and doubts that you would like to sort out. If something is bothering you, ask yourself why and see if you can find a solution. Can you talk to someone else about it?

If things are really getting you down, ask yourself how you are coping. It is difficult for anyone to admit that they aren't coping properly. However, doing so does show tremendous inner strength, which other people will appreciate. It is also often the first step to finding a solution. Either way, opening up to someone you trust can be a massive help.

*A very emotional time can have more ups and downs than a rollercoaster ride. You may be left feeling drained and exhausted. Whether or not you come out smiling is up to you.*

# COPING WITH PRESSURE

When it comes to feelings and emotions, it is important to strike a balance between knowing when it is okay to conceal them, and recognising when it is time to share them with others. This area of life skills has a great effect on the way others see us.

*Is a friend truly a friend when they pressure you into doing something you know is dangerous or that you really don't want to do?*

## Peer pressure

Besides dealing with our own, internal pressures, people also have to deal with pressure from their peers. This is when you feel pressure from people of your own age to say or do things. Peer pressure can be positive, such as urging each other to improve in a sport. But it can be negative if you are pressured into doing things that are wrong.

## Getting it Wrong

When a really stressful situation crops up, such as bullying or prejudice, you may have difficulty managing your feelings. But you must try not to lose control. Do not:

- think it's your fault or that you deserve it.

- ignore it and hope it will go away – it probably won't.

- hit out, retaliate, or get into a fight.

- put yourself in situations where it happens. Do this by avoiding certain people.

- show that you are upset or scared.

Peer pressure can involve all sorts of things, such as copying schoolwork, lying, vandalism, even getting involved with racial, sexual, or other **abuse** and **prejudice**. While it is perfectly natural to want to fit in and be liked by your friends, try to be true to yourself when faced with negative peer pressure.

## Getting it Right

Have a think about ways of getting to know yourself better and establishing your own identity. For example, make a list of personal qualities or **traits** that you admire in others. Then work out what you'd like to include in your own actions and behaviour. Would you like to be:

• happy and smiling much of the time?

• cool and in control?

• a good listener?

• loyal to friends?

• someone with interesting hobbies?

Get to know the reasons for and ways of saying "no".

• If you know inside that what is happening is wrong, go with your feelings and beliefs that you know are right. Do not betray yourself.

• If you feel negative pressure, discuss matters with one or a few friends who might feel the same way. That way, you can support each other.

• "Choose your friends wisely" is not just an empty old saying. Consider whether you're going around with the wrong crowd, who may have different beliefs and values to you.

• When you do say "no", do it with confidence. Be ready to talk about, or do, something else straightaway.

## MAKE FRIENDS, KEEP FRIENDS

True friendships are a thing of value. Friends make life a pleasure rather than a chore. Making and keeping friends gives us a warm feeling inside, and this shows in a positive, happy outside. The ability to make friends is one of life's major skills and has a huge influence on the way others view and treat us.

### Give and take

Real friendship, especially with people your own age, is a two-way business. It's give and take, share and share alike. Helping someone else, and then being helped in turn, makes us feel needed and happy.

Most people interact with several social groups, such as their own family, neighbours, classmates at school, members of a group or club, and so on. Friends can come from any of these areas. Usually "best friends" are about the same age as you, but not always.

Sometimes you may not notice that a friendship is developing, in which case it's probably because it is so easy and natural. As you slip into a good friendship, you may notice that certain things no longer seem important. A true "best friend" does not worry if you don't have the latest trainers or you make an occasional mistake.

*Good friends are caring and sharing with each other. They often have similar tastes or, if not, are keen to listen to each other's suggestions.*

*"My best friend is the
one who brings out the
best in me."*
*Henry Ford (1863–1947),
American industrialist*

## "Friends" that aren't

Sometimes people may try to become
your friend, but they have a hidden
reason for doing so. You might even
feel uncomfortable when talking to
a particular person. This could be
an adult who seems to be overly
familiar. Little children are taught
about "stranger danger", but everyone
should be aware of it, regardless of
age. Beware, and if you're worried that
a relationship doesn't feel right, talk
to a trusted adult, such as a teacher,
who is not closely connected with the
person concerned.

### Getting it
# Right

One tactic for making friends
is to counter bad peer
pressure and act as a focus
for your own group. See
how others react when the
bad peers are around, trying
to pressure them. Do they
seem to feel like you? Make
a casual mention to them,
such as "I'm just not into
that, maybe trying this
instead would be better?".
They may start to have a
chat and firm up a friendship
with you and each other.
Soon you could have a new
peer group of friends.

# A Time Of Change

The early teenage years are a time when the human body goes through many changes between childhood and young adulthood. During **puberty** the body grows and develops rapidly over a period of two to four years.

## THE BASICS

Puberty involves growing up through many physical, emotional, and social changes, to become an adult. The changes of puberty are programmed into the body's **genetic** instructions. They are based on body chemistry, especially involving natural substances called **hormones**. Hormones control how body parts grow and work. They can also have an effect on your behaviour.

Puberty may seem hard to cope with, but take comfort: everyone goes through it, and gets through it. Serious long-term problems associated with puberty are very rare. Understanding what happens during puberty can help you feel more confident and able to impress others with how well you are coping.

### DID YOU KNOW?

Each human body is unique, and so is the time of puberty. It can happen anytime, usually from the age of 11–18. Likewise, the time it takes varies greatly.

## Getting it Right

As you go through puberty, people may make thoughtless remarks and comments. At a sensitive time, this can trigger real anxiety. These thoughts and actions can help.

- Reassurance: everyone goes through puberty, it's normal. Look around – friends of your age are probably all at some stage of puberty.

- Don't blame: you're not a victim or at fault, it's simply nature taking its course.

- Not a life sentence: it won't last forever, the worst is usually over in just a few months.

- Be grown-up about it: you can show your increasing maturity by rising above cheap jokes.

## Puberty problems

Puberty can be frustrating. It happens at a time when we are becoming more aware of our appearance and how we look. Yet the changes of puberty seem to mess up how we look, with skin spots, awkward body proportions, and clumsy movements. This can make you feel worried on the inside that you don't look good on the outside.

*The fast growth of puberty can mean young people of the same age, who have been similar heights for years, quickly become very different heights. This is not odd – it's quite normal.*

## Mood swings

There are plenty of upheavals during puberty and the wider time of **adolescence**. Apart from the physical changes, there are mental ones, too. Emotions are felt more strongly. You may experience mood swings, from feeling overjoyed to very sad in just a few minutes, for no obvious reason. You may spend lots more time worrying about social relationships and whether you are popular and well liked. You may feel doubtful or experience feelings of hopelessness, inadequacy, and an inability to cope.

## SPOTS AND SNIFFS

During puberty, oily skin means spots and pimples (such as blackheads, whiteheads, and boils) are prone to regularly appear. Body smells also become more noticeable during puberty. With a few sensible actions you can keep all of these things under control, feel better about yourself, and keep looking good.

### Grease is the word

Because of hormonal changes during puberty, the skin's microscopic sebaceous **glands** produce more of the natural oily substance, **sebum**, than normal. This keeps skin supple and waterproof, and protects against germs. But too much sebum tends to make skin and hair feel greasy.

It often also blocks the tiny pits, or **follicles**, from which hairs grow, and clogs up sweat pores. As sebum collects, **microbes** breed in it. This can make skin red and irritated, as well as producing unpleasant body odours.

### Acne

Acne is complicated. It may even run in the family. Rarely, some creams or medicines, such as steroids, can make it worse. Humid atmospheres (such as sweaty changing rooms) and oily substances are also not good news for acne. There are dozens of anti-acne medications, which most people find effective. It may take a few attempts to find the best one. For cases of extreme acne, see a doctor.

### Getting it Right

Skin care is a very personal matter, but also a simple one. All you need is:

- hot soapy water,
- something to gently rub away the grease and dirt (such as a soft sponge or flannel),
- not too much rubbing, as this can irritate or break the skin,
- no spot-squeezing, as this encourages infection and can cause scarring,
- a clean towel.

## Keeping clean

Good hygiene is important during puberty. This should at least include a daily shower, bath, or all-over wash.

Hair care – washing and brushing – is also important. Whatever your style, greasy, tangled, dirty, unkempt hair is a turn-off for most people. Neglect your hair, and you will also be neglecting your scalp. This can lead to dandruff – tiny flakes of skin falling from the scalp. Medicated, anti-dandruff shampoos are usually effective. Although, as with most skincare products, you may need to try a few before finding one that suits.

*Washing doesn't just get you clean and sniff-free. It refreshes your face, unblurs your eyes, and gives you a fresh, ready-to-go feeling.*

Don't forget your fingernails. Dirty, chewed nails are not very attractive, and many nasty germs can harbour there. Scrub your hands regularly, with a nail brush when possible.

And there's oral hygiene. People are quick to notice discoloured teeth and bad breath, so brush and floss each morning after breakfast and last thing before bed.

(If you have sensitive or allergic skin, carefully check products before use.)

Shop shelves are packed with men's grooming products – aftershaves, skin toners, moisturisers, facepacks, bodywashes, skin detoxers, fake tans. But do they work? Most will have some sort of benefit, but make sure you read what they say and do very carefully. A cream that "makes your skin appear smoother" will not magically disappear spots and lumps. Such products can also be expensively packaged and costly. However, they can be useful. Moisturisers can help to control patches of dry, flaky or itchy skin and "smellies" (such as aftershaves) are favoured by some. These should never be used as a substitute for soap and water. Mixed with pungent body odour, they can produce a truly horrible whiff!

# ALL IN THIS TOGETHER

The major thought to hold onto is that you are not alone. Teenagers have been going through puberty for thousands of years. It happens to everyone. You may choose to keep your worries and doubts to yourself, but if you decide to talk about them with good friends, you'll probably find that they are going through the same things as you. Sharing problems can ease the burden and give you back your confidence and **self-esteem**.

## Male changes

The changes each person experiences vary during puberty. Generally, boys experience an increase in height of about 30 cm (12 in.) over a two-year period. Their limbs become longer in proportion to head and body, they develop muscle bulk, and their body outline becomes more angular, as the shoulders widen and hips become narrower. Other noticeable changes are oily skin, a deeper voice, and thick hair growing on the face, underarms, chest and pubic area.

## Female changes

During puberty, a girl's body grows in height and her limbs become longer. Breasts form and enlarge, and the body outline becomes more curved. Thick hair grows on underarms and the pubic area, skin becomes oily, the voice deepens slightly, and **periods** begin.

## DID YOU KNOW?

There are many myths about puberty. Scientific evidence has shown that none of the following myths are true.

- Certain foods or drinks, such as lots of milk, make puberty start earlier.

- Too many fast-food meals or greasy foods (such as chips), make spots worse.

- Dreaming about sex causes acne.

- Sexual stimulation and actions worsen your eyesight.

- Boys who go through puberty late, end up smaller and weaker.

- Late puberty means less chance of boys being fathers.

- Don't worry if you gain lots of weight during puberty, you'll "grow into" it.

*Everyone gets at least some spots from acne and they often soon go. Regular thorough washing and an approved acne skin cream are the best solutions, not cover up make-up and squeezing.*

# Role Models

Most of us have one, two, or even a few people we admire as role models. We look up to them with respect and approve of what they do. We might even want to be like them. But this is a tricky area. Often role models are famous, rich, and powerful – for example, sport, music, movie, or fashion stars. These people have numerous publicity and public relations staff to control their image and the way they are seen. The image they collectively project is simply unattainable for just one individual.

## MEDIA FRENZY

It is difficult – probably impossible – to avoid the media. Almost every day we can encounter television, newspapers, books, magazines, the Internet, radio, downloads, advertisements, sponsorships, 24-hour rolling news. But how does the media and advertising affect us?

In particular, how do we view the celebrities, superstars and fashion models we see every day in magazines, on televisions, and in other media? Do we want to be like them – even if we don't realise it?

The media and the celebrity business are harsh worlds. We often hear that people are built up and become famous, only to be knocked down again, and this is so often true. In these worlds, image is everything, but of course image is not real life. It has limits and drawbacks.

### Getting it Wrong

Many people prey on teenagers who want to be famous. Merion wanted to be a model. When he was 17, a friend of a friend persuaded him to try a modelling agency she knew. Merion didn't know much about the agency, but he was keen on the girl, so went along. The agency told him he might have "something", took a few photos of him, and got him to sign a contract. Next month, he received a massive bill for the photos and no work ever came.

## Coping with fame

Some people cannot cope with the pressures and demands of fame. Perhaps they are in the public eye simply for their looks. Are they really contented and happy?

So often, stories about people's problems can soon take over from accounts of their achievements. Perhaps they are used as pawns or stooges in a power struggle, for example, between rival television channels or magazines. A fast rise can be met with an equally fast and tragic fall.

For these kinds of reasons, we should be very careful about admiring celebrities and wanting to be like them. Just a quick peek behind the gloss and glamour shows that short-term fame, often for just a week or month, is not a quick fix to feeling good inside.

*A studio is a very specialised, pressurised place. Some people behave quite differently in front of the camera. They may seem likeable and friendly on-screen, but can be the opposite in "real life".*

## Why them?

Next time you see a celebrity-type magazine, television programme, or website, take a few moments to think. For each person, ask yourself – why is she or he there? Perhaps there is a serious, valid reason, such as having true talent or attaining a great achievement. This is worth some respect and approval.

What about other so-called celebrities? Some might be in a well-known, super-rich or royal family. Others may be famous due to a quirk of fate, such as winning the lottery. Still others are in the magazine because they are paid to be. Are any of those in these latter groups really worthy of your respect and admiration? If so, what is it about them that you admire?

Imagine the same people in a year's time. Will they still be famous then? When considering role models, a more realistic approach is to consider people who you know in real life. To earn our respect and admiration, real role models must be genuine and sincere. Usually these people are much closer to home – and can often be found among your family, friends, peers, and social groups.

*Even the most ordinary people can have the most extraordinary and amazing experiences to relate. Take a little time to get to know them – they may earn your respect as a result.*

## Getting it Right

You might get some insight into what makes a **role model** by imagining yourself as suddenly becoming famous, and a role model for thousands of young people. What would you try to do? Being honest and straightforward pays off in the long run, as untruths are often found out. No one is a fan of rudeness, so being polite and thoughtful would keep admirers on your side. People that try to be something or someone they are not often let people down when their true self shows through. Being yourself is always best. But could you do all of this easily and naturally, whilst coping with the immense pressures and stresses of fame and celebrity? Maybe being a true role model is not as easy as it first seems?

## WHO DO YOU ADMIRE?

1) **You are looking for advice on what to wear to a party. Do you:**
   a) ask your close friends about what they are wearing?
   b) look through a fashion magazine for a celebrity style to copy?
   c) ask your fashionable sibling for help?

2) **You have no plans and it's Friday night. Are you most likely to:**
   a) meet up with some friends?
   b) watch some late-night TV?
   c) stay at home with your family?

3) **You've been on holiday with your family. Coming home, you're most looking forward to:**
   a) seeing your friends?
   b) catching up with the news?
   c) eating a home-cooked meal?

4) **You are stranded on a desert island. What is it you miss most:**
   a) your friends?
   b) celebrities?
   c) your family?

See page 50 to find out what kind of person you're likely to admire.

# LOOK AGAIN

Feeling good and looking good means thinking about what to wear. Some people throw on any old clothes, others cannot get dressed until they have thought through every detail of their appearance. Are you like one of these examples, or somewhere in between? Understanding your own interest in clothes and fashion, and where you rank them in the general importance of things, helps you to feel comfortable about what you wear.

## WHAT TO WEAR

Keeping up with the latest fashion may seem important. But what is fashionable and what isn't? For some, being anti-fashion is a fashion. Whatever your style, designer labels come and go and styles move on all the time. How you wear your clothes is as important as what you wear.

### Wear it well

If you are confident in your clothing style or look, you can always find out about when and why it developed. If you can talk with knowledge, explain the style, and show people how and why you are interested, they are more likely to respond. However, don't go too far. Keep it simple and low key, especially to begin with. Taking a particular clothing style to an extreme is more likely to attract negative comments. This can be damaging to your self-esteem, which you may or may not be able to handle.

## DID YOU KNOW?

Money management is tricky to learn. When some 15–18s were asked about their spending:

• 9 out of 10 saw credit cards as "easy money" with no idea how to pay them off.

• 1 in 20 thought credit cards don't have to be paid back.

• 1 in 4 assumed their parents would take responsibility for their debts.

The advice? Be realistic about what you spend – fashion doesn't have to come at a cost.

Source: UK Bankruptcy Information Centre

*Some styles are perceived as extremes and it can be easy to lay stereotypes on the wearers. Try not to take people at face value – you may be surprised.*

## The right label?

Fashions and styles might indicate what kind of music a person listens to or what kind of attitude he or she has. Fashion labels are often pinned to a particular style.

Sometimes people may make snap judgements about others based on their clothes, hair, shoes, piercings, or other features. Often, such judgements are inaccurate. But if you adopt a style in this way, prepare for people who might form a quick opinion based on your appearance. If you understand this is happening, you can then be ready to show them the person underneath and why you look the way you do.

**TIP**

You may like a fashion, but can you afford it? Specialist clothes, trainers, and designer label accessories are usually very costly. Try finding the styles you like in charity or vintage clothing shops. If having the latest and greatest is most important, you also have to appreciate that you may have to cut back spending on something else.

## SKIN DeeP

Are looks and beauty skin deep? Some people are naturally attractive on the outside, in appearance, and also inside, in their personality. But there are all kinds of combinations, and outer looks are definitely no guarantee of the person within. Remember, the old saying "it's what's on the inside that counts" generally holds true.

Everyone has skin features such as birthmarks, moles, and freckles. Similarly, everyone has their own individual skin tone. Being accepting, happy, and confident about your own skin helps you interact with other people. When you are at ease, they are at ease, too.

## DID YOU KNOW?

Some people with light skin feel that a suntanned look is more healthy and attractive. But too much exposure to the sun is far from healthy. Ultraviolet rays can be a serious health risk. Think in the long term, too. Harmful rays make the skin wrinkle early and increase the chances of skin growths and cancers. Is having a tan worth these long-term risks?

## Who likes what?

Next time you are chatting with friends, have a discussion about "body add-ons", such as those listed below. Which are most popular? Which would your friends really have? You might be surprised by all the different views.

- Dyed hair

- A very prominent hairstyle, such as a mohawk

- Temporary (wear-off) tattoos

- A permanent tattoo

- An ear stud

- Multiple ear piercings, with studs, rings, chains, and plugs

- Body piercings, such as eyebrow, lip, tongue, or navel.

## Think unique

If you wish to change your body, think hard about why you want to change it, who you are changing it for, and what people's reactions may be to you if you change. Permanent alterations, such as tattoos, should be given extra thought, as they are just that: permanent. Piercings, though they can be removed, often leave scars.

There are many, many people who get tattoos and piercings as a way of making themselves stand out as an individual. Sometimes you can be more unique by not copying them.

# Getting it
# Wrong

Nathan's 18th birthday party involved him and some friends going to see a movie and then going on to a restaurant for pizza. However, as it grew later, talk turned to risk-taking and thrill-seeking. Fred liked extreme sports. Ashan got his thrills from Internet gaming. Natty loved his band and music. Nathan – well, he hadn't really thought about it … Nathan is now 32. At that party, his friends dared him to get a tattoo of his girlfriend's name. He did. Now he's ready to get married – to someone else. Nathan plans to have the tattoo removed, which will be a lot more uncomfortable, time-consuming, and costly than if he had just said "no".

*Our lives, likes, and loves change over the years. Tattoos, on the other hand, don't: they are permanent.*

## no one's perfect!

Fame, money, good looks, an outstanding talent – even having all of these together – do not guarantee health and happiness. Rather, happiness depends on where we direct our energies. It is a state of mind. Success in life's little struggles helps us to feel more confident and positive inside, which then shows through to the outside.

### Looking back

We cannot alter past aspects of our lives, such as family background, where we grew up, and whether we were rich or poor. But we can reflect on it **constructively**. Try to think of positives, such as a supportive parent or relation, a good childhood friend, a success at school, and happy times, such as holidays.

### Looking forward

Instead of looking back to what cannot change, look forward to future achievements. In particular, don't put up with nagging doubts. If you're worried about hanging out with doubtful "friends", dabbling in bad habits, or not getting a good job, take action!

There are many sources of help, from a chat with an encouraging family member, to teachers and professionals, such as sports coaches and careers experts. If these people see that you are sincere,

### Getting it Right

Have you ever thought of using your abilities to help others? Activities such as mentoring, helping, and counselling can be hugely rewarding. For example, if you're good at reading, you could volunteer to help a slow reader, or someone who has trouble with words. The same applies if you have an ability for maths, sport, music – almost anything. Helping others can be hugely rewarding, and just what the doctor ordered when it comes to feeling positive about your own life!

they will respond with help and encouragement, and you will soon be heading towards a positive future!

### Signs of trouble

Abusing drugs or alcohol affects how a person feels inside. This feeds through to outward behaviour and appearance. As well as physical signs (bloodshot eyes, unsteadiness, slurred or nervous speech), there may be behavioural changes in a person who turns to alcohol or drugs.

Drugs and alcohol have a devastating effect on your body, looks, and social skills. If someone is affected by alcohol or drug use they:

- become more withdrawn and preoccupied.
- lose interest in previously enjoyed activities.
- experience mood swings and become emotional, nervous, aggressive, or depressed.
- miss school, work, or appointments.
- are often short of money, avoid paying for things, and ask for loans.
- avoid direct eye contact.
- change their tastes in friends, clothes, and appearance.
- disappear for long periods, with excuses that don't add up.
- seem more prone to accidents or injuries.
- make excuses – problems are always someone else's fault.

*Making good friends, sharing passions, and gaining a sense of belonging, help us feel happier and fulfilled.*

# INSIDE, OUTSIDE

How you feel inside has enormous effects on how you look on the outside. This does not simply mean your physical features, clothes, and hairstyles. It's about how you look around, walk and move, smile and frown, listen and talk. It's about whether you are friendly, helpful, interesting and good to know. In turn, this determines how people see you and react to you, and what they think of you as a person.

How do you feel about yourself? And how do you think others see you? Are you always happy and confident, or constantly sad and worried? Do you look forward to every day as a new challenge with fresh opportunities, or do you wake up each morning fearing the hard slog to come? Are you pleased with your abilities, your family and friends, your school, and general situation, or do you continually wish you were someone else, somewhere else? Maybe you are somewhere in between these extremes. Perhaps you change your opinion from day to day.

## Inward focus

No one can see into your private mind and read your innermost thoughts. Only you can know them. And you can only know them by thinking about areas of life with care and honesty, and being truthful to yourself. Knowing yourself is an early part of the process of feeling good on the inside, and one of life's major skills.

In turn, if you feel good within, that's a long way on the road to looking great to others. The two feed on and reinforce each other. Being true to yourself, and at ease with your thoughts and feelings, are inner aspects that feed through strongly to how other people view you and what the world thinks of you.

## Positive outlook

Everyone has strengths, abilities and talents. Some are clear, such as being great at sport, art, or music. Others are less obvious, such as social and people-based skills. Social skills that are important, but difficult to recognise in ourselves, include:

- being easy to talk to, with conversation that flows naturally rather than being dominated by one person.

- making well-informed, safe choices rather than unreliable, off-the-cuff decisions.

- showing an interest in what others think and do, but at the same time having your own point of view and being able to express your opinions.

- thinking of others, for example, showing concern and trying to help when they have problems.

 If you get to know yourself, you'll find others will want to, too.

"Fate chooses your relations, you choose your friends."

Jacques Delille (1738–1813), French poet

### ARE YOU A HEALTHY EATER?
**For page 17**

**If you mostly answered:**

**a)** You may be on the road to an eating disorder. You feel tired because you are missing vital nutrients. It's time to take control of your body before it takes control of you.

**b)** You may be on the road to becoming overweight. You snack throughout the day and do not eat properly, meaning you are likely to experience mood swings.

**c)** You are a healthy eater. You are likely to respect your body and what you put into it.

### WHAT TYPE OF SPORT?
**For page 25**

**If you mostly answered:**

**a)** You don't appear to like being on your own. You would probably enjoy team sports, but don't let that stop you from trying to get to know yourself better by trying solitary sports.

**b)** Any sport will do! You are a team player, but you also enjoy being on your own. Try out different challenges to see which you enjoy best.

**c)** You probably would enjoy solitary sports, but don't let that stop you from making new friends by joining a team!

### WHO DO YOU ADMIRE?
**For page 41**

**If you mostly answered:**

**a)** You look to your friends for inspiration and are likely to admire them.

**b)** You surround yourself with images from the media and celebrities are important to you. It's likely that you admire celebrities.

**c)** Family is important to you. You are likely to find role models in close family members.

# (20) Things To Remember

1 Be honest with yourself. Don't try to convince yourself that something is okay when you really know deep inside that it is not okay.

2 Give and take. Helping others gives you a great feeling inside. Likewise, accepting help makes you feel wanted and others feel good.

3 Recognise your strengths and use them wisely. Everyone is good at something – it is just a matter of realising what that something is.

4 Eat a varied diet, especially plenty of fresh fruits and vegetables, to keep your body healthy.

5 Take enough exercise to give your body the action it needs, and to know that you're doing what you can to look after it.

6 Value true friends that like you for who you are.

7 Beware those who try to persuade you to do things against your will, even after you have explained the reasons why you're not willing.

8 Think about others. For example, remember their likes and dislikes, and details such as birthdays.

9 Open up when you need to. For example, discuss problems with family members and friends.

10 Be sensitive to the feelings of others. People who are going through a bad time, or suffering problems, tend to lose their sense of humour. So making "clever" jokes about their situation will not be helpful.

11 Be a good listener as well as a good talker.

12 Think before you act, and avoid taking unnecessary risks.

13 You can get plenty of thrills and excitement from safer, controlled situations.

14 Everyone has limitations. Get to know yours, but don't dwell on the unfairness of them.

15 Focus on the positives and what you can do well.

16 Understand that the media bombard people with advertisements, images, and information that may create an impossible ideal.

17 Don't solve problems by lying, abusing others, or through using violence. There's always another way to work it through.

18 If you are the victim of bullying, prejudice, or similar, don't think it's your fault. Tell someone you trust who will help.

19 Stop and think now and again about yourself, your situation, your family and friends.

20 Remember that feeling positive is in your mind and your body – and up to you!

# Further Information

## WEBSITES

**http://www.eatwell.gov.uk/healthydiet/**
The UK Government's main healthy eating website, with masses of information on how to keep your body well and working properly by eating the right foods.

**http://www.sportandme.com/docs/sports/beginners/index.html**
How to find a sport that suits you, with articles, tips, and advice on dozens of sports – written by keen amateurs and knowledgeable professionals.

**http://kidshealth.org/kid/grow/body_stuff/puberty.html**
Plenty of easy to understand information on puberty, what happens, why, and when.

**http://www.rolemodel.net/**
A site promoting the idea that every person can inspire those around them by looking outward, being helpful, and spreading hope through daily actions.

**http://www.imnotobsessed.com/**
See how quickly the celebrity world changes and how short-lived it can be.

**http://www.succeedsocially.com/philosophy**
A site about how to move from feeling awkward to content and happy in company, includes lots of friend-making tips.

**http://www.kidscape.org.uk/cyberbullying/**
Guidelines and advice about cyberbullying and online safety from the first UK charity established specifically to prevent bullying and child sexual abuse.

**http://teens.drugabuse.gov/**
Created by the US National Institute on Drug Abuse (NIDA), to educate young people (as well as their parents and teachers) on the science behind drug abuse.

## BOOKS

*Acne for Dummies*, Herbert P. Goodheart, M.D. (John Wiley & Sons, 2006)

*Bringing Up Your Parents: A Guide for Teenagers*, John Farman (Piccadilly Press Ltd, 2005)

*Building Self-Confidence For Dummies:* Kate Burton and Brinley Platts (John Wiley and Sons Ltd, 2005)

*Do the Right Thing: A Teenager's Survival Guide for Tricky Situations,* Jane Goldman (Piccadilly Press, 2007)

*Get Strong!: Body, by Jake's Guide to Building Confidence, Muscles, and a Great Figure,* Jake Steinfeld (Topeka Bindary, 2002)

*Healthy Eating for Kids: Over 100 Meal Ideas, Recipes and Healthy Eating Tips for Children,* Anita Bean (A & C Black Publishers, 2007)

# DISCUSSION TOPICS

### Whose heroes?
Next time you are with good friends, have a chat about the people you admire.
- How long have you had these role models?
- What do you admire in particular about them?
- Do you think you'll still have the same view in a few months or a year?

### What a worry!
A recent US poll revealed some of the topics parents and carers worry about in their teenage sons and daughters. Here are a few – what are your views?
- Sex education and reducing teenage pregnancy.
- Can after-school programmes increase physical activity?
- Does a daily breakfast make you healthier?
- Are social networking sites endangering young teens?
- What stresses teens out?

# GLOSSARY

**abuse** mistreatment, either physical or emotional

**additives** substances that are added to a food, rather than being contained in the original food

**adolescence** the time period between being a child and an adult, includes puberty and usually takes up most of the teenage years

**allergy** condition in which the body has an exaggerated response to a substance

**blood pressure** the pressing force of blood as it pushes on the walls of its tubes, the blood vessels

**blood vessels** tubes which carry blood away from the heart, around the body, and back to the heart

**calories** an older measurement of energy or work, now replaced by joules

**carbohydrates** substances containing carbon, hydrogen, and oxygen; in the diet, they are mostly foods rich in starches and sugars

**cardiac** to do with the heart. The cardiac muscles cause the heart's powerful pumping actions.

**constructively** in a helpful way

**counsellor** person who gives guidance

**dietary supplements** substances, such as vitamins or minerals, which can be taken in the form of pills, drinks, or similar, when a person cannot eat a full healthy diet

**endorphins** natural body substances produced in and near the brain, which help to dull pain and give a sense of feeling good

**facilities** in sport, the equipment, such as changing rooms, courts, and pitches, needed to take part

**fats** substances which are oily or fatty; in the diet, they are found in animal and vegetable products

**fibre** tough substances ("roughage") in the diet that cannot be digested for energy or nutrients, but that help the health of the digestive system

**flushing** when the skin goes redder as a result of tiny surface blood vessels becoming wider, so more blood than usual flows through, to help cool the body or as a result of embarrassment

**follicles** tiny pit-like pockets in the skin, from which hairs grow

**genetic** to do with genes: chemical instructions (as DNA, deoxyribonucleic acid), inherited from our parents, that tell the body how to develop and maintain itself

**gland** a body part that makes a substance and releases it, such as a sweat gland in the skin, or salivary glands that make saliva (spit)

**hormones** natural substances, made in the body by hormonal glands, that are released into the blood to control the workings of other parts

**kit** in sports, equipment needed to take part, such as clothing items, footwear, and a helmet or bat

**microbes** tiny living things, visible only through a microscope

**minerals** substances in the diet, such as iron, calcium, and sodium, which are needed for healthy body parts and processes, such as blood, bones, and nerves

**optimistic** being positive and looking on the bright side, rather than being negative or pessimistic

**periods** in females, the time of the reproductive or menstrual cycle when the thickened, blood-rich lining of the womb (uterus) breaks down and leaves the body, through the vagina

**prejudice** a preconceived opinion, which is not based on facts

**preoccupied** when someone seems worried about something

**proteins** substances of which there are thousands of kinds that form parts of cells and tissues. Especially found in meaty foods.

**puberty** the rapid growth and development of the body, usually taking two to four years, as it changes from child to young adult

**role model** someone who is viewed as an example of a certain kind of behaviour or attitude, and who other people wish to be like

**saturated fats** fatty, greasy, or oily parts of foods that can cause health problems, especially heart disease

**sebum** a natural waxy, oily skin substance, made in the sebaceous glands, that keeps skin supple

**self-esteem** feeling of self-worth, self-confidence, and self-respect

**sprains** when joints move in an unusual way, becoming swollen and painful

**traits (personality)** features or aspects of someone's personality and behaviour

**vitamins** in the diet, substances needed for healthy body processes, such as making new blood, repairing wounds, and fighting germs and illness

# Index